ACT® Elements

High School Science
Student Workbook

MasteryPrep

Inquiries concerning this publication should be mailed to:

MasteryPrep
7117 Florida Blvd.
Baton Rouge, LA 70806

MasteryPrep is a trade name and/or trademark of Ring Publications LLC.
This publication, its author, and its publisher are in no way affiliated with or authorized by ACT Inc. ACT® is a copyright and/or trademark of ACT Inc.

10 9 8 7 6 5 4 3 2 1

ISBN-13: 978-1-948846-48-6

Table of Contents

Get ready to master the ACT and Aspire tests

You are about to participate in the most effective and broadly used test prep program for ACT and Aspire in the nation! With Elements, you will learn the most frequently tested content on the ACT and Aspire tests and develop the skills and strategies necessary to achieve the score you desire.

With practice in all four subjects, you will be fully prepared.

The Science Elements workbook is just one part of a larger program that includes four core subjects, each in line with a subtest found on both the ACT and Aspire tests: English, math, reading, and science. Each workbook builds your mastery of the content most frequently tested by providing hundreds of ACT and Aspire practice questions and activities. By completing this book, you will be prepared for the science subtest; the rest of the program will prepare you for the English, reading, and math subtests.

The score you want is within your reach!

The ACT and Aspire tests are rigorous, challenging, marathon exams. They can be intimidating. Each year many students who take these tests feel that it is impossible to prepare for them—that whatever score they earn is the best they can do. The MasteryPrep program has proven this assumption to be completely false. Students dedicated to the program routinely see substantial improvement on their test scores. It will take hard work and determination, but with the content and strategies available to you, anything is possible.

Additional resources are at your fingertips.

To round out your study, tips on both ACT and Aspire test prep and strategy are available on the MasteryPrep website. Visit http://masteryprep.com/act-tips-blog/ to access additional information about time management, how the ACT and Aspire are scored, smarter guessing, and more.

You *can* master the ACT and Aspire test.

The keys to success with test preparation are content, practice, and strategy. As your teacher leads you through the practice and activities, focus on the content. Participate and ask questions to clarify any points of confusion.

Give your best effort on every question no matter how hard or easy it may seem. Complete any homework your teacher assigns and make sure you ask questions if you do not fully understand a concept.

Finally, as you develop content mastery and practice the ACT and Aspire questions, work on building your test-day strategy. Look for trends in the questions and answer choices, determine your strongest and weakest areas, and decide how you will pace yourself on the day of the test.

Good luck!

4 △ △ △ △ △ △ △ △ △ **4**

Set 1 Exercise 1

Passage I

Ecological succession is the way species change composition in an area over time. For example, a grassland may eventually become populated by trees.

Ecologists have conducted a study of Brazilian rainforests that have been subjected to slash-and-burn agriculture. The Brazilian natives burn the rainforest and use the resulting highly fertilized land for farming. After many years, wildlife and vegetation begin to return to the area.

Table 1 shows the various bird species, dominant (most prevalent) plants, as well as the successional time in years of various plots of rainforest subjected to slash-and-burn agriculture.

The estimated changes in net productivity (measured as grams of organic mass produced per square meter per year [g/m²/yr]) of plants on the plots of land studied are shown on Figure 1. Note that the successional periods are indicated at the bottom of the chart and are named based on the dominant plants during each time period.

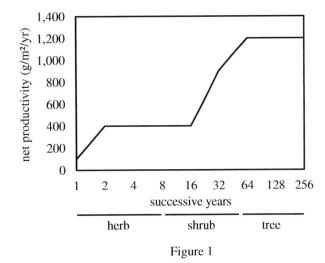

Figure 1

4 △ △ △ △ △ △ △ △ △ 4

Table 1									
Successional time (yr)	1	5	15	20	25	35	60	100	150
bird species \ dominant plants	weeds	grasses	shrubs		small trees				canopy trees
Ground thrush	X	X							
Boatbill		X	X						
Cicada bird			X	X					
Cockatoo			X	X	X				
Friarbird			X	X					
Quail			X	X					
Scrubwren					X	X	X	X	
Noisy pitta					X	X	X	X	
Wompoo pigeon					X	X	X	X	
Brown pigeon						X	X	X	
Sacred ibis						X	X	X	
Straw-necked ibis						X	X	X	X
Yellow-faced honeyeater						X	X	X	
Spotless crake								X	X
Dollarbird							X	X	X
Channel-billed cuckoo								X	X
Black-faced cuckoo-shrike								X	X
Darter								X	X
Emerald dove									X

A shaded box indicates that birds were present in a density of at least one pair per 20 acres.

4 △ △ △ △ △ △ △ △ △ 4

Set 1 Exercise 2

1. How many different bird species are listed on Table 1 ?
   - **A.** 8
   - **B.** 12
   - **C.** 14
   - **D.** 19

2. After six years of successional time, about how much organic mass is produced per square meter per year?
   - **F.** 110 g/m²/yr
   - **G.** 410 g/m²/yr
   - **H.** 500 g/m²/yr
   - **J.** 800 g/m²/yr

3. What is the dominant plant 100 years after farmland is subjected to slash-and-burn agriculture?
   - **A.** Canopy trees
   - **B.** Small trees
   - **C.** Shrubs
   - **D.** Grasses

4 △ △ △ △ △ △ △ △ 4

Set 1 Exercise 3

1. According to Figure 1, which of the following time periods produces the least organic mass per square meter per year?

   A.   1 to   4 successional years
   B.   8 to 16 successional years
   C. 16 to 32 successional years
   D. 128 to256 successional years

2. About how much organic mass is produced per square meter per year after two years of successional time?

   F.   200 g/m²/yr
   G.   400 g/m²/yr
   H. 1,000 g/m²/yr
   J. 1,600 g/m²/yr

3. According to Table 1, how many years does it take for small trees to become dominant on farmland subjected to slash-and-burn agriculture?

   A.   5 years
   B. 10 years
   C. 15 years
   D. 25 years

4 △ △ △ △ △ △ △ △ △ 4

Set 1 Exercise 4

1. Based on Table 1, classify each bird species as present in a density of at least one pair per 20 acres during shrub plant dominance **or** tree growth dominance. Write in the blank which category each bird species belongs to.

   dollarbird _____

   cicada bird _____

   quail _____

   scrubwen _____

2. Based on the introductory material in the passage, choose the phrases that correctly describe slash-and-burn agriculture. Write in the blank next to each statement to indicate whether it is supported or unsupported by the passage.

   Burning existing plant life results in fertile land. _____

   Net productivity is measured in $m/g^2/yr$. _____

   Vegetation can never return to slash-and-burn areas. _____

   Slash-and-burn areas are used for farming. _____

   Rainforests have too much precipitation for slash-and-burn agriculture. _____

   Ecological succession can occur in slash-and-burn areas. _____

4 △ △ △ △ △ △ △ △ △ **4**

Set 1 Exercise 5

1. Write a paragraph describing which birds you think will be present after 150 years and why.

Set 2 Exercise 1

Passage VII

Both solids and liquids typically have the property of expanding when heated. Two experiments were conducted by chemists to study the expansion of various substances. In the first experiment, five 1-meter wires were hung vertically from the ceiling. An electric current was passed through each wire to heat them from 0°C to 120°C. The length of each wire was measured and recorded in 20-degree increments. The results of this study are shown in Figure 1.

In the second experiment, designed to test the expansion of various liquids, four different solutions were placed in 1-meter tall graduated burets. The liquids were heated at the same rate from 20°C to 60°C, and the increase in volume was measured in 5-degree increments. The results of this experiment are shown in Figure 2.

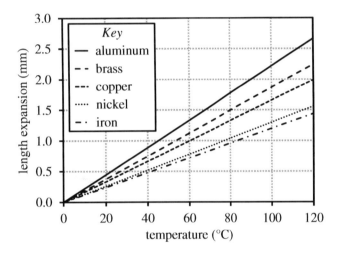

Figure 1

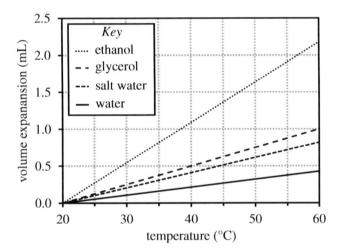

Figure 2

4 △ △ △ △ △ △ △ △ △ 4

Set 2 Exercise 2

1. About how many millimeters did the brass wire expand at 60°C ?

   A. 0.9 mm
   B. 1.0 mm
   C. 1.1 mm
   D. 1.3 mm

2. At what temperature did ethanol expand exactly 1.0 mL ?

   F. 30°C
   G. 38°C
   H. 40°C
   J. 57°C

3. What liquid had the smallest rise at 40°C ?

   A. Ethanol
   B. Water
   C. Salt water
   D. Glycerine

4   **4**

Set 2 Exercise 3

1. Which of the following wires expanded the least at 80°C ?

   A. Brass
   B. Nickel
   C. Copper
   D. Aluminum

2. What was the largest amount of expansion measured on a wire in Figure 1 ?

   F. 1.9 mm
   G. 2.2 mm
   H. 2.7 mm
   J. 3.0 mm

3. Which of the following temperatures created the greatest rise in salt water?

   A. 25°C
   B. 35°C
   C. 45°C
   D. 55°C

4 △ △ △ △ △ △ △ △ △ 4

Set 2 Exercise 4

1. A student hypothesizes that if the first experiment were repeated at higher temperatures, the brass wire would have a larger expansion than the aluminum wire at 130°C. Use the results of the first experiment and the data presented in Figure 1 to explain why the student's hypothesis is **UNSUPPORTED** by the results of the experiment. As part of your explanation, give your own prediction of the approximate expansions of the brass and aluminum wires at 130°C.

4 △ △ △ △ △ △ △ △ △ 4

Set 2 Exercise 4

2. Based on the passage, give **ONE** difference between the first and second experiments. Be sure to compare **BOTH** experiments in your answer.

4 △ △ △ △ △ △ △ △ 4

Set 2 Exercise 5

1. Why do you think the chemists hung the wires vertically from the ceiling in the first experiment? What would have changed and how would the results have been affected by a different positioning of the wires?

4 △ △ △ △ △ △ △ △ △ 4

Set 3 Exercise 1

Passage III

Several recent health studies point to excessive sodium intake as a contributing factor to various health problems. Sodium is typically added to food in the form of table salt (NaCl). Students performed two experiments to measure the sodium levels of various canned goods.

Experiment 1

Four solutions, each containing a different amount of dissolved NaCl (table salt) were prepared in water. A coloring agent that reacts with sodium to form a blue compound that strongly absorbs light of a specific wavelength was added to each solution before they were all diluted to 100 mL with water. A control solution was also prepared with no NaCl added. The students used a *colorimeter* (a device used to measure how much light of a selected wavelength is absorbed by a sample) in order to determine the *absorbance* of each solution. The absorbances were then corrected by subtracting the absorbance of the control solution from each reading. The results are shown in Table 1.

Experiment 2

After being drained, 100-gram samples of various canned vegetables were ground in a blender with 50 mL of water. The resulting mixture was filtered, and then diluted to 100 mL with water. The students added the coloring agent to each solution. Then they measured the absorbance of each solution using the colorimeter, with the results shown in Table 2.

Table 1		
Concentration of Na^+ (ppm)	Measured absorbance	Corrected absorbance
0.0	0.1	0.0
1.0	0.2	0.1
2.0	0.3	0.2
4.0	0.5	0.4
8.0	0.9	0.8

Table 2		
Canned goods	Corrected absorbance	Concentration of Na^+ (ppm)
Green beans	0.552	5.52
Corn	0.439	4.39
Carrots	0.024	0.24
Mixed vegetables	0.123	1.23

4   **4**

Set 3 Exercise 2

1. What was the measured absorbance of the solution of sodium at 4 ppm ?

   A. 0.1
   B. 0.2
   C. 0.5
   D. 0.9

2. If another sodium solution had a measured absorbance of 0.4, what would its corrected absorbance be?

   F. 0.1
   G. 0.2
   H. 0.3
   J. 0.4

3. What was the concentration of Na^+ when the corrected absorbance was 0.439 ?

   A. 0.439
   B. 0.552
   C. 4.39
   D. 5.52

4   **4**

Set 3 Exercise 3

1. According to Table 1, what is the corrected absorbance of a sodium solution with a concentration of 8 ppm ?

   A. 0.4
   B. 0.5
   C. 0.8
   D. 0.9

2. Which canned good had the highest concentration of Na^+ ?

   F. Green beans
   G. Corn
   H. Carrots
   J. Mixed vegetables

3. What was the corrected absorbance of the corn solution?

   A. 0.024
   B. 0.439
   C. 0.552
   D. 4.39

4 △ △ △ △ △ △ △ △ △ 4

Set 3 Exercise 4

1. A student claimed that a solution with a concentration of Na^+ of 5.0 ppm will have a lower measured absorbance than a solution with a 1.0 ppm concentration of Na^+. Based on the results of Experiment 1, explain why the student's claim was **INCORRECT**. As part of your explanation, give your prediction for an approximate measured absorbance for a solution with a 5.0 ppm concentration of Na^+.

4 △ △ △ △ △ △ △ △ △ **4**

Set 3 Exercise 4

2. Based on the data presented in Table 2, examine each claim to see if it correctly describes the corrected absorbance and concentration of Na^+ in the tested canned goods. Write in the blank next to each statement to indicate whether it is supported or unsupported by the passage.

Canned peaches have a lower concentration of Na^+ than canned carrots. _____

Canned corn and canned carrots have the same corrected absorbance. _____

Canned green beans have a higher corrected absorbance than canned carrots. _____

Canned mixed vegetables have a lower concentration of Na^+ than canned corn. _____

Canned carrots have a corrected absorbance of 0.123. _____

Canned corn has a higher concentration of Na^+ than canned carrots. _____

4 △ △ △ △ △ △ △ △ △ 4

Set 3 Exercise 5

1. In the description of Experiment 1, the passage states that each solution was diluted to 100 mL. Write a paragraph explaining why the students did this and what effect it had on the experiment.

Set 4 Exercise 1

A team of researchers built a greenhouse with three separate artificially lighted and heated sections. During one of their experiments, the researchers measured and recorded the weekly average light intensity (in arbitrary units) as well as the weekly average air temperature (in °C). The results for the five-week long experiment are provided in Table 1 and Table 2.

Table 1			
	Weekly average light intensity		
Week	Section 1	Section 2	Section 3
1	290.3	84.9	120.3
2	307.1	79.8	80.7
3	315.2	76.9	76.8
4	305.3	73.9	69.6
5	312.2	70.2	75.1

Table 2			
	Weekly average air temperature (°C)		
Week	Section 1	Section 2	Section 3
1	19.68	19.08	18.65
2	20.11	19.23	18.48
3	20.75	19.19	18.64
4	21.02	19.51	18.98
5	21.15	19.61	19.12

4 △ △ △ △ △ △ △ △ △ 4

Set 4 Exercise 2

1. What was the lowest average weekly air temperature recorded during the study?
    A. 13.74 °C
    B. 18.48 °C
    C. 19.68 °C
    D. 21.15 °C

2. What was the average light intensity of Section 3 in Week 3 ?
    F. 69.6
    G. 76.8
    H. 76.9
    J. 80.7

3. What was the total change in average air temperature from Week 3 to Week 4 in Section 3 ?
    A. −0.34 °C
    B. +0.34 °C
    C. +1.24 °C
    D. None of the above

4 △ △ △ △ △ △ △ △ △ 4

Set 4 Exercise 3

1. What was the highest average weekly air temperature recorded during the study?

   A. 18.48°C
   B. 19.68°C
   C. 21.15°C
   D. 24.91°C

2. What section experienced the largest overall change in temperature during the study?

   F. Section 1
   G. Section 2
   H. Section 3
   J. None of the above

3. What section had the largest fluctuation of average light intensity between Weeks 1 and 2 ?

   A. Section 1
   B. Section 2
   C. Section 3
   D. None of the above

4 △ △ △ △ △ △ △ △ △ **4**

Set 4 Exercise 4

1. In Section 1 of the greenhouse, as the weeks increased, did the weekly average air temperature increase, decrease, or stay the same? Explain your answer using numbers from the table.

4 △ △ △ △ △ △ △ △ △ 4

Set 4 Exercise 4

2. A student claims that if all three sections are tested for weekly average air temperature for a 6th week, Section 1 would likely have an average air temperature of 18.25°C. Based on the data in Table 2, explain why the student's claim is **UNLIKELY**. As part of your explanation, give your prediction of the weekly average air temperature in Section 1 at Week 6.

4 △ △ △ △ △ △ △ △ △ 4

Set 4 Exercise 5

1. Imagine you are tasked with expanding upon this experiment. Write a paragraph describing what you would add to the experimental procedures or what new elements you would introduce. What would you hope to learn from the results of your addition?

4 △ △ △ △ △ △ △ △ △ **4**

Set 5 Exercise 1

Scientists have found that carbon monoxide gas (CO) is toxic when it exceeds concentrations of 0.1% by volume. In urban areas, automobiles are a significant source of CO. Studies have shown that CO levels in cities are higher during colder weather. A group of students hypothesized that cars emit more CO in colder air temperatures than in warmer air temperatures during the first 18 minutes after they are started. The students then performed two experiments to test their hypothesis.

Experiment 1

A hose was connected to the tailpipe of a car. After the engine was started, the exhaust was collected in a leak-proof bag. From there, a 10-mL sample was taken from the bag with a syringe and injected into a *gas chromatograph*, which separates mixed gases into their individual components. The students then were able to determine the percentage by volume of CO present in the exhaust. Samples were taken at 3-minute intervals, with the last sample taken 18 minutes after the engine was started. This experiment was conducted on four different vehicles with an external air temperature of $-7°C$. The results of this experiment are shown in Table 1.

Experiment 2

The same study was conducted on the same four cars at an external temperature of $22°C$. The results of this experiment are shown in Table 2.

Table 1				
Time after starting (min)	Percent of CO in exhaust at $-7°C$			
	1980 Model A	1980 Model B	2008 Model A	2008 Model B
3	3.4	3.3	1.3	0.2
6	4.1	7.2	1.1	1.3
9	4.4	11.1	0.6	2.6
12	3.8	7.3	0.5	3.2
15	3.3	6.9	0.4	1.9
18	3.0	6.8	0.4	1.7

Table 2				
Time after starting (min)	Percent of CO in exhaust at $22°C$			
	1980 Model A	1980 Model B	2008 Model A	2008 Model B
3	2.1	2.0	0.4	1.0
6	3.5	6.3	0.4	1.5
9	1.5	7.1	0.3	0.8
12	1.0	6.1	0.1	0.3
15	1.0	4.9	0.1	0.3
18	0.9	4.7	0.1	0.2

4 △ △ △ △ △ △ △ △ △ 4

Set 5 Exercise 2

1. At what minute mark did the CO percentage of the exhaust reach 1.3 in the 2008 Model A at −7°C ?

   A. 3 minutes
   B. 6 minutes
   C. 9 minutes
   D. 12 minutes

2. What percent of CO was present in the exhaust of the 1980 Model A at −7°C after 6 minutes?

   F. 3.3%
   G. 4.1%
   H. 4.4%
   J. 7.2%

3. What vehicle had the lowest level of CO in the exhaust compared to the other vehicles?

   A. 1980 Model A
   B. 1980 Model B
   C. 2008 Model A
   D. 2008 Model B

Set 5 Exercise 3

1. What vehicle had the lowest level of CO present in the exhaust after 18 minutes at −7°C ?

    A. 1980 Model A
    B. 1980 Model B
    C. 2008 Model A
    D. 2008 Model B

2. At what minute mark did the CO percentage of the exhaust reach 1.5 in the 1980 Model A at 22°C ?

    F. 6 minutes
    G. 9 minutes
    H. 12 minutes
    J. 15 minutes

3. What was the difference between the percentage of CO in the exhaust of the 1980 Model B after 6 minutes at the temperature of −7°C compared to the percentage of CO in its exhaust at the temperature of 22°C after the same amount of time elapsed?

    A. 0.7%
    B. 0.8%
    C. 0.9%
    D. 1.2%

4 △ △ △ △ △ △ △ △ △ **4**

Set 5 Exercise 4

1. Based on Tables 1 and 2, does the data on the 2008 Model A support, contradict, or not pertain to the student hypothesis that cars emit more CO at colder temperatures? Explain your answer using numbers from the table.

4 △ △ △ △ △ △ △ △ △ **4**

Set 5 Exercise 4

2. Based on Table 2, order the three car models below from the car having the lowest percentage of CO in its emission at 15 minutes to the car having the highest percentage of CO in its emission at 15 minutes. Write 1, 2, or 3 in the blanks.

1980 Model A _____

2008 Model A _____

2008 Model B _____

4 △ △ △ △ △ △ △ △ △ **4**

Set 5 Exercise 5

1. Imagine you are among the students performing these experiments. Write a paragraph describing what you would do to change or improve either experiment and why.

4   **4**

Set 6 Exercise 1

A group of students performed two experiments with a microscope using 4 different objective lenses.

Experiment 1

The students viewed four different slides through each objective lens. They labeled the slides A, B, C and D. Each slide had two thin lines painted on it with varying degrees of separation between them. For each objective lens, the students determined whether the lines could be seen as separate or were blurred together into one. They put the results from their experiment into Table 1.

Experiment 2

To further test their lenses, the students prepared a slide with a line on it that was exactly 0.1 mm thick. This they called their *object size*. They viewed the slide with each of their objective lenses and estimated how long the line appeared to them, which they called their *image size*. Finally, the student calculated the *magnification (M)* of each lens by using the following formula:

M = image size ÷ object size.

The data from their experiment appears in Table 2.

Table 1				
	Objective lens			
Slide	1	2	3	4
A	▓	▓	▓	▓
B	▓	▓	▓	
C	▓	▓		
D	▓			

A shaded box indicates the lines were blurred together. An empty box indicates that the lines appeared separate.

Table 2		
Objective lens	Image size (mm)	M
1	5	50
2	10	100
3	25	250
4	50	500

4 △ △ △ △ △ △ △ △ △ 4

Set 6 Exercise 2

1. What was the image size of Objective Lens 1 ?
   A. 5 mm
   B. 10 mm
   C. 25 mm
   D. 50 mm

2. What objective lens caused the lines on Slide D to be blurred together?
   F. Objective Lens 1
   G. Objective Lens 2
   H. Objective Lens 3
   J. Objective Lens 4

3. How many slides were blurred by Objective Lens 2 ?
   A. 1
   B. 2
   C. 3
   D. 4

4   **4**

Set 6 Exercise 3

1. Which slide was Objective Lens 2 able to display with separation between its lines?

   A. Slide A
   B. Slide B
   C. Slide C
   D. Slide D

2. What slide's lines did not appear separate with any objective lens?

   F. Slide A
   G. Slide B
   H. Slide C
   J. Slide D

3. What was the magnification of Objective Lens 2 ?

   A. 10
   B. 50
   C. 100
   D. 250

4 △ △ △ △ △ △ △ △ △ 4

Set 6 Exercise 4

1. A fifth lens is tested as in Experiment 2, and its magnification is found to be 25. Use the results of Experiments 1 and 2 to predict which slides would be viewed through this lens as lines that appeared to be blurred together. Explain how you used the results to make your prediction.

4 △ △ △ △ △ △ △ △ △ 4

Set 6 Exercise 4

2. Based on description of Experiment 2 only:

Is how long the line appeared when viewed through a lens called the object size, the image size, or the magnification?

Indicate the actual size of the line on the slide.

4 △ △ △ △ △ △ △ △ △ 4

Set 6 Exercise 5

1. How can the experiment described in the passage be improved? Identify a specific change (or changes) you would make and how that would increase the accuracy of the results.

4 △ △ △ △ △ △ △ △ △ **4**

Set 7 Exercise 1

Passage I

Ecological succession is the way species change composition in an area over time. For example, a grassland may eventually become populated by trees.

Ecologists have conducted a study of Brazilian rainforests that have been subjected to slash-and-burn agriculture. The Brazilian natives burn the rainforest and use the resulting highly fertilized land for farming. After many years, wildlife and vegetation begin to return to the area.

Table 1 shows the various bird species, dominant (most prevalent) plants, as well as the successional time in years of various plots of rainforest subjected to slash-and-burn agriculture.

The estimated changes in net productivity (measured as grams of organic mass produced per square meter per year [g/m²/yr]) of plants on the plots of land studied are shown on Figure 1. Note that the successional periods are indicated at the bottom of the chart and are named based on the dominant plants during each time period.

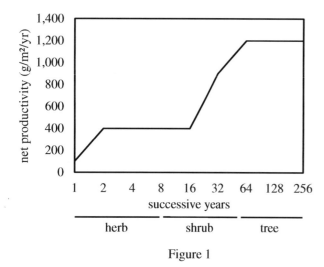

Figure 1

4 △ △ △ △ △ △ △ △ △ 4

Table 1									
Successional time (yr)	1	5	15	20	25	35	60	100	150
bird species \ dominant plants	weeds	grasses	shrubs		small trees				canopy trees
Ground thrush	■	■							
Boatbill		■	■						
Cicada bird			■	■					
Cockatoo			■	■	■				
Friarbird			■	■					
Quail			■	■					
Scrubwren					■	■	■	■	
Noisy pitta					■	■	■	■	
Wompoo pigeon					■	■	■	■	
Brown pigeon						■	■	■	
Sacred ibis						■	■	■	
Straw-necked ibis						■	■	■	■
Yellow-faced honeyeater						■	■		
Spotless crake								■	■
Dollarbird							■	■	■
Channel-billed cuckoo								■	■
Black-faced cuckoo shrike								■	■
Darter								■	■
Emerald dove									■

A shaded box indicates that birds were present in a density of at least one pair per 20 acres.

4 △ △ △ △ △ △ △ △ △ **4**

Set 7 Exercise 2

1. The boatbill is present in a density of at least one pair per 20 acres at the same time that two different types of plants are dominant. What are these plants?

   A. Weeds and grasses
   B. Grasses and shrubs
   C. Shrubs and small trees
   D. Small trees and canopy trees

2. What is the only bird species on this chart that is present in a density of at least one pair per 20 acres at the same time that weeds are the dominant plant category?

   F. Black-faced cuckoo-shrike
   G. Dollarbird
   H. Straw-necked ibis
   J. Ground thrush

3. What is the most productive stage of succession, according to Figure 1 ?

   A. Herb stage
   B. Shrub stage
   C. Tree stage
   D. All of the above

4 △ △ △ △ △ △ △ △ **4**

Set 7 Exercise 3

1. How many different bird species are present in a density of at least one pair per 20 acres at the same time that small trees are the dominant plant category?

   A. 9
   B. 12
   C. 13
   D. 15

2. According to this chart, how many years does it take before the emerald dove appears in densities of at least one pair per 20 acres on farmland that was subjected to slash-and-burn agriculture?

   F. 35 years
   G. 60 years
   H. 100 years
   J. 150 years

3. About how many years of successional time will it take for a plot of land subjected to slash-and-burn agriculture to reach an average net productivity of 500 g/m²/yr ?

   A. 4 years
   B. 8 years
   C. 16 years
   D. 20 years

4 △ △ △ △ △ △ △ △ △ **4**

Set 7 Exercise 4

1. Based on the table, give **ONE** difference between the years when shrubs were dominant and the years when trees were dominant. Be sure to compare **BOTH** types in your answer.

4 △ △ △ △ △ △ △ △ △ 4

Set 7 Exercise 4

2. Another bird species, the keel-billed toucan, is found to be present in a density of at least one pair per 20 acres at a time when canopy trees are dominant. Use the data in the passage to predict an approximate net productivity for the plot of rainforest land subjected to slash-and-burn agriculture when the keel-billed toucan is found present. Explain how you used the data to make your prediction.

4 △ △ △ △ △ △ △ △ △ **4**

Set 7 Exercise 5

1. Write a paragraph explaining, in your own words, how the rainforest changed over the 150 years after being subjected to slash-and-burn agriculture.

4 △ △ △ △ △ △ △ △ △ 4

Set 8 Exercise 1

Passage VII

Both solids and liquids typically have the property of expanding when heated. Two experiments were conducted by chemists to study the expansion of various substances. In the first experiment, five 1-meter wires were hung vertically from the ceiling. An electric current was passed through each wire to heat them from 0°C to 120°C. The length of each wire was measured and recorded in 20-degree increments. The results of this study are shown in Figure 1.

In the second experiment, designed to test the expansion of various liquids, four different solutions were placed in 1-meter tall graduated burets. The liquids were heated at the same rate from 20°C to 60°C, and the increase in volume was measured in 5-degree increments. The results of this experiment are shown in Figure 2.

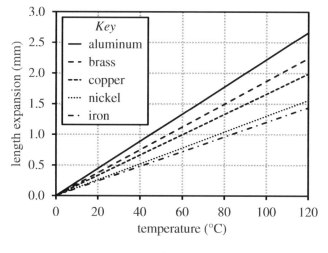

Figure 1

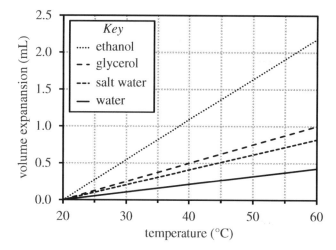

Figure 2

4   **4**

Set 8 Exercise 2

1. Which wire expanded the most at 120°C ?

   A. Copper
   B. Aluminum
   C. Brass
   D. Iron

2. Which liquid had the greatest volume expansion at 50°C ?

   F. Ethanol
   G. Water
   H. Salt water
   J. Glycerol

3. Which two wires expanded equally at 20°C ?

   A. Copper and brass
   B. Iron and nickel
   C. Aluminum and iron
   D. Copper and aluminum

4   **4**

Set 8 Exercise 3

1. What was the smallest amount of expansion measured on a wire in Figure 1 ?
   A. 0.00 mm
   B. 0.05 mm
   C. 0.10 mm
   D. 0.15 mm

2. At what temperature did all of the liquids rise equally?
   F. 20°C
   G. 25°C
   H. 30°C
   J. 40°C

3. Which of the following temperatures created the least rise in water?
   A. 20°C
   B. 25°C
   C. 35°C
   D. 40°C

4 △ △ △ △ △ △ △ △ △ 4

Set 8 Exercise 4

1. Look at the graphs in the passage. Classify each substance below as having the highest expansion or lowest expansion compared to the other substances tested in its given experiment. Write what category the substance belongs to in the blank.

   water _____

   iron _____

   aluminum _____

   ethanol _____

4 △ △ △ △ △ △ △ △ △ 4

Set 8 Exercise 4

2. Based on the passage, give **ONE** similarity between the first and second experiments. Be sure to compare **BOTH** experiments in your answer.

4 △ △ △ △ △ △ △ △ △ 4

Set 8 Exercise 5

1. Write a paragraph describing some practical applications for knowing about the expansion rates of wires made of various materials. Why is this useful information? Who might use the results of this experiment, and how?

4 △ △ △ △ △ △ △ △ △ 4

Set 9 Exercise 1

Passage III

Several recent health studies point to excessive sodium intake as a contributing factor to various health problems. Sodium is typically added to food in the form of table salt (NaCl). Students performed two experiments to measure the sodium levels of various canned goods.

Experiment 1

Four solutions, each containing a different amount of dissolved NaCl (table salt) were prepared in water. A coloring agent that reacts with sodium to form a blue compound that strongly absorbs light of a specific wavelength was added to each solution before they were all diluted to 100 mL with water. A control solution was also prepared with no NaCl added. The students used a *colorimeter* (a device used to measure how much light of a selected wavelength is absorbed by a sample) in order to determine the *absorbance* of each solution. The absorbances were then corrected by subtracting the absorbance of the control solution from each reading. The results are shown in Table 1.

Experiment 2

After being drained, 100-gram samples of various canned vegetables were ground in a blender with 50 mL of water. The resulting mixture was filtered, and then diluted to 100 mL with water. The students added the coloring agent to each solution. Then they measured the absorbance of each solution using the colorimeter, with the results shown in Table 2.

Table 1		
Concentration of Na⁺ (ppm)	Measured absorbance	Corrected absorbance
0.0	0.1	0.0
1.0	0.2	0.1
2.0	0.3	0.2
4.0	0.5	0.4
8.0	0.9	0.8

Table 2		
Canned goods	Corrected absorbance	Concentration of Na⁺ (ppm)
Green beans	0.552	5.52
Corn	0.439	4.39
Carrots	0.024	0.24
Mixed vegetables	0.123	1.23

4   **4**

Set 9 Exercise 2

1. What was the corrected absorbance of the solution of sodium at 8 ppm ?

   A. 0.0
   B. 0.1
   C. 0.2
   D. 0.8

2. What was the measured absorbance of the solution of sodium at 0 ppm ?

   F. 0.0
   G. 0.1
   H. 0.2
   J. 0.5

3. What was the corrected absorbance of the mixed vegetables solution?

   A. 0.024
   B. 0.123
   C. 0.439
   D. 1.23

4 △ △ △ △ △ △ △ △ △ 4

Set 9 Exercise 3

1. What canned good had a concentration of Na^+ between 4 and 5 ppm ?

   A. Green beans
   B. Corn
   C. Carrots
   D. Mixed vegetables

2. What is the corrected absorbance if the measured absorbance is 0.9, according to Table 1 ?

   F. 0.4
   G. 0.5
   H. 0.8
   J. 0.9

3. Which canned good had the lowest concentration of Na^+ ?

   A. Green beans
   B. Corn
   C. Carrots
   D. Mixed vegetables

4 △ △ △ △ △ △ △ △ △ 4

Set 9 Exercise 4

1. Based on the passage, give **ONE** similarity between Experiment 1 and Experiment 2. Be sure to compare **BOTH** experiments in your answer.

4 △ △ △ △ △ △ △ △ △ 4

Set 9 Exercise 4

2. Based on the introductory material in the passage:

- Is the measured absorbance a measure of absorbed water, absorbed salt, or absorbed light?
- Identify the device used to measure this absorbance.

4 △ △ △ △ △ △ △ △ △ 4

Set 9 Exercise 5

1. In describing Experiment 1, the passage states that a control solution was prepared with no NaCl. Write a paragraph explaining the purpose of a control in an experiment and why this solution functioned as the control for the experiment described in the passage.

4   **4**

Set 10 Exercise 1

A team of researchers built a greenhouse with three separate artificially lighted and heated sections. During one of their experiments, the researchers measured and recorded the weekly average light intensity (in arbitrary units) as well as the weekly average air temperature (in °C). The results for the five-week long experiment are provided in Table 1 and Table 2.

Table 1			
	Weekly average light intensity		
Week	Section 1	Section 2	Section 3
1	290.3	84.9	120.3
2	307.1	79.8	80.7
3	315.2	76.9	76.8
4	305.3	73.9	69.6
5	312.2	70.2	75.1

Table 2			
	Weekly average air temperature (°C)		
Week	Section 1	Section 2	Section 3
1	19.68	19.08	18.65
2	20.11	19.23	18.48
3	20.75	19.19	18.64
4	21.02	19.51	18.98
5	21.15	19.61	19.12

4 △ △ △ △ △ △ △ △ △ **4**

Set 10 Exercise 2

1. What was the lowest average light intensity recorded during the study?

   A. 18.48
   B. 46.8
   C. 69.6
   D. 315.2

2. What was the average light intensity of Section 1 in Week 4 ?

   F. 21.02
   G. 290.3
   H. 305.3
   J. 307.1

3. What section had the smallest fluctuation of average light intensity between Weeks 4 and 5 ?

   A. Section 1
   B. Section 2
   C. Section 3
   D. None of the above

4   **4**

Set 10 Exercise 3

1. What was the average air temperature of Section 2 in Week 2 ?

   A. 18.48°C
   B. 19.19°C
   C. 19.23°C
   D. 20.11°C

2. What section had a weekly average air temperature of 20.15 °C in Week 5 ?

   F. Section 1
   G. Section 2
   H. Section 3
   J. None of the above

3. What was the average air temperature of Section 1 in Week 2 ?

   A. 18.48°C
   B. 19.19°C
   C. 19.23°C
   D. 20.11°C

4 △ △ △ △ △ △ △ △ △ 4

Set 10 Exercise 4

1. Based on Table 2, order the 3 sections below from the section having the smallest temperature range to the section having the largest temperature range. Write 1, 2, or 3 in the blank.

Section 1 _____

Section 2 _____

Section 3 _____

4 △ △ △ △ △ △ △ △ **4**

Set 10 Exercise 4

2. Based on the passage, give **ONE** difference between Table 1 and Table 2. Be sure to compare **BOTH** tables in your answer.

4 △ △ △ △ △ △ △ △ △ 4

Set 10 Exercise 5

1. A local farmer is building a new greenhouse for one of his crops. Write a paragraph describing how the famer could use the data from this experiment to influence his greenhouse design.

4 △ △ △ △ △ △ △ △ △ **4**

Set 11 Exercise 1

Scientists have found that carbon monoxide gas (CO) is toxic when it exceeds concentrations of 0.1% by volume. In urban areas, automobiles are a significant source of CO. Studies have shown that CO levels in cities are higher during colder weather. A group of students hypothesized that cars emit more CO in colder air temperatures than in warmer air temperatures during the first 18 minutes after they are started. The students then performed two experiments to test their hypothesis.

Experiment 1

A hose was connected to the tailpipe of a car. After the engine was started, the exhaust was collected in a leak-proof bag. From there, a 10-mL sample was taken from the bag with a syringe and injected into a *gas chromatograph*, which separates mixed gases into their individual components. The students then were able to determine the percentage by volume of CO present in the exhaust. Samples were taken at 3-minute intervals, with the last sample taken 18 minutes after the engine was started. This experiment was conducted on four different vehicles with an external air temperature of –7°C. The results of this experiment are shown in Table 1.

Experiment 2

The same study was conducted on the same four cars at an external temperature of 22°C. The results of this experiment are shown in Table 2.

Table 1				
Time after starting (min)	Percent of CO in exhaust at –7°C			
	1980 Model A	1980 Model B	2008 Model A	2008 Model B
3	3.4	3.3	1.3	0.2
6	4.1	7.2	1.1	1.3
9	4.4	11.1	0.6	2.6
12	3.8	7.3	0.5	3.2
15	3.3	6.9	0.4	1.9
18	3.0	6.8	0.4	1.7

Table 2				
Time after starting (min)	Percent of CO in exhaust at 22°C			
	1980 Model A	1980 Model B	2008 Model A	2008 Model B
3	2.1	2.0	0.4	1.0
6	3.5	6.3	0.4	1.5
9	1.5	7.1	0.3	0.8
12	1.0	6.1	0.1	0.3
15	1.0	4.9	0.1	0.3
18	0.9	4.7	0.1	0.2

4   4

Set 11 Exercise 2

1. What vehicle had the highest level of CO in the exhaust compared to the other vehicles?

   A. 1980 Model A
   B. 1980 Model B
   C. 2008 Model A
   D. 2008 Model B

2. At what minute mark did the CO percentage of the exhaust reach 6.3 in the 1980 Model B at 22°C ?

   F. 6 minutes
   G. 9 minutes
   H. 12 minutes
   J. 15 minutes

3. What percent of CO was present in the exhaust of the 1980 Model B at –7°C after 9 minutes?

   A. 3.3%
   B. 7.3%
   C. 6.9%
   D. 11.1%

4 △ △ △ △ △ △ △ △ △ 4

Set 11 Exercise 3

1. What vehicle had the highest level of CO present in the exhaust after 12 minutes at 22°C ?

   A. 1980 Model A
   B. 1980 Model B
   C. 2008 Model A
   D. 2008 Model B

2. What vehicle had a time period with a higher level of CO in the exhaust at 22°C than at −7°C ?

   F. 1980 Model A
   G. 1980 Model B
   H. 2008 Model A
   J. 2008 Model B

3. At what minute mark did the CO percentage of the exhaust reach 1.7 in the 2008 Model B at −7°C ?

   A. 9 minutes
   B. 12 minutes
   C. 15 minutes
   D. 18 minutes

4 △ △ △ △ △ △ △ △ **4**

Set 11 Exercise 4

1. Based on the passage, choose the statements that correctly describe carbon monoxide gas as tested in the experiments. In the blank next to each statement, indicate if it is supported or unsupported by the passage.

Car exhaust was tested for CO emissions at −10°C and 32°C. _____

Carbon monoxide gas is toxic at air concentrations of over 0.1% in volume. _____

Four different models of cars were tested in both experiments. _____

Carbon monoxide levels are lower in some cities during colder weather. _____

A gas chromatograph was used to measure CO levels in car exhaust. _____

Samples of CO were taken at 5 minute intervals. _____

4 △ △ △ △ △ △ △ △ △ 4

Set 11 Exercise 4

2. Examine the data presented in the passage. Classify each of the following factors as described by the passage as contributing to higher levels of CO in the air or not contributing to higher levels of CO in the air. Write what category (contributes to higher levels or does not contribute to higher levels) the factor belongs to in the blank.

Cold weather _____

Warm weather _____

Chromatograph _____

Car exhaust _____

4 △ △ △ △ △ △ △ △ △ 4

Set 11 Exercise 5

1. Was the student hypothesis described in the introduction of the passage supported by the results of the experiments? Why or why not? Write a paragraph explaining your answer.

4   **4**

Set 12 Exercise 1

A group of students performed two experiments with a microscope using 4 different objective lenses.

Experiment 1

The students viewed four different slides through each objective lens. They labeled the slides A, B, C and D. Each slide had two thin lines painted on it with varying degrees of separation between them. For each objective lens, the students determined whether the lines could be seen as separate or were blurred together into one. They put the results from their experiment into Table 1.

Experiment 2

To further test their lenses, the students prepared a slide with a line on it that was exactly 0.1 mm thick. This they called their *object size*. They viewed the slide with each of their objective lenses and estimated how long the line appeared to them, which they called their *image size*. Finally, the student calculated the *magnification (M)* of each lens by using the following formula:

M = image size ÷ object size.

The data from their experiment appears in Table 2.

Table 1				
	\multicolumn{4}{c} Objective lens
Slide	1	2	3	4
A	▓	▓	▓	▓
B	▓	▓	▓	
C	▓	▓		
D	▓			

A shaded box indicates the lines were blurred together. An empty box indicates that the lines appeared separate.

Table 2		
Objective lens	Image size (mm)	M
1	5	50
2	10	100
3	25	250
4	50	500

4 △ △ △ △ △ △ △ △ **4**

Set 12 Exercise 2

1. What objective lens did not cause the lines on Slide B to be blurred together?

   A. Objective Lens 1
   B. Objective Lens 2
   C. Objective Lens 3
   D. Objective Lens 4

2. What was the image size of Objective Lens 4 ?

   F. 5 mm
   G. 10 mm
   H. 25 mm
   J. 50 mm

3. Which two objective lenses displayed the lines on Slide C as separate?

   A. Objective Lenses 1 and 2
   B. Objective Lenses 2 and 4
   C. Objective Lenses 3 and 4
   D. Objective Lenses 1 and 3

4 △ △ △ △ △ △ △ △ △ 4

Set 12 Exercise 3

1. What was the image size of Objective Lens 3 ?
   A.   5 mm
   B.   10 mm
   C.   25 mm
   D. 250 mm

2. Which lens had the greatest magnification?
   F. Objective Lens 1
   G. Objective Lens 2
   H. Objective Lens 3
   J. Objective Lens 4

3. What was the magnification of Objective Lens 4 ?
   A.   10
   B.   50
   C. 100
   D. 500

4 △ △ △ △ △ △ △ △ △ 4

Set 12 Exercise 4

1. A student claimed that a lens with a magnification of 200 would have an image size of 35 mm. Based on the results of Experiment 2, explain why the student's claim was **INCORRECT**. As part of your explanation, give the correct image size of this lens.

4 △ △ △ △ △ △ △ △ △ 4

Set 12 Exercise 4

2. Based on the passage, give **ONE** difference between the description of Experiment 1 and Experiment 2. Be sure to compare **BOTH** experiments in your answer.

_____

_____

_____

_____

_____

_____

_____

_____

_____

_____

_____

_____

_____

_____

_____

_____

_____

_____

4 △ △ △ △ △ △ △ △ △ 4

Set 12 Exercise 5

1. The passage does not indicate a control is used for either experiment. Describe a possible control that could have been used for either Experiment 1 or 2 and why it would be effective.

4 △ △ △ △ △ △ △ △ △ **4**

Set 13 Exercise 1

Students in a physics class used 2 different methods to calculate the total stopping distance of a vehicle (Z). Z is the total distance a vehicle travels from the time the driver first reacts to the emergency all the way until the car comes to a complete stop.

In Method 1, X is the distance a car travels during the driver's assumed reaction time of 0.75 seconds. Y is the average distance traveled once the brakes are applied.

Method 2 simply assumes that Z is the initial speed in feet per second times 2 seconds. (Z = speed × 2). Table 1 shows X, Y, and Z for several different initial speeds, where Z is calculated using both methods. Figure 1 is a graph of Z versus initial speed for Methods 1 and 2.

Table 1					
Initial speed (mi/hr)	Initial speed (ft/sec)	Method 1			Method 2
		X(ft)	Y(ft)	Z(ft)	Z(ft)
25	36	28	25	53	72
50	74	56	100	156	148
75	110	84	275	359	220
100	148	112	450	562	298

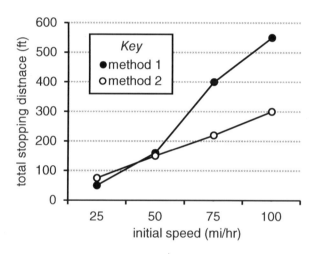

Figure 1

4 △ △ △ △ △ △ △ △ △ 4

Set 13 Exercise 2

1. Per Method 1, what is the total stopping distance for a car with an initial speed of 25 mi/hr ?

   A. 53 ft
   B. 72 ft
   C. 220 ft
   D. 359 ft

2. According to Method 1, which of the following quantities is closest to the distance that a car would travel with an initial speed of 60 miles per hour?

   F. 100 ft
   G. 150 ft
   H. 250 ft
   J. 350 ft

3. During the driver's assumed reaction time, how far does the car travel with an initial speed of 25 mi/hr ?

   A. 25 ft
   B. 28 ft
   C. 53 ft
   D. 72 ft

4   **4**

Set 13 Exercise 3

1. Per Method 1, what is the total stopping distance
    for a car with an initial speed of 110 ft/sec ?

    A. 110 ft
    B. 220 ft
    C. 298 ft
    D. 359 ft

2. What is the difference between the calculation of
    total distance traveled in Method 1 and Method 2
    for an initial speed of 148 ft/sec ?

    F. 184 ft
    G. 264 ft
    H. 298 ft
    J. 562 ft

3. Per Method 1, what is the total stopping distance
    for a car with an initial speed of 36 ft/sec ?

    A. 25 ft
    B. 28 ft
    C. 53 ft
    D. 72 ft

4 △ △ △ △ △ △ △ △ △ 4

Set 13 Exercise 4

1. Based on the passage:
   - Does Table 1 use Y to represent the total stopping distance of a vehicle, the initial speed times two, or the average distance once brakes are applied?
   - Identify the assumed reaction time used in Method 1.

4 △ △ △ △ △ △ △ △ 4

Set 13 Exercise 4

2. Based on the passage, choose the statements that correctly describe the experiments carried out. Write in the blank next to each statement to indicate whether it is supported or unsupported by the passage.

In Method 2, X is the initial speed in feet per second times 2 seconds.

_____

In Method 1, Y is the average distance traveled once the brakes are applied.

_____

Y is the total distance a vehicle travels from the time the driver first reacts to the emergency to the time the car comes to a complete stop.

_____

X is the distance a car travels during the driver's assumed reaction time of 0.75 seconds.

_____

Figure 1 is a graph of total stopping distance versus initial speed for Methods 1 and 2.

_____

Table 1 shows the results of Method 1 only.

_____

4 △ △ △ △ △ △ △ △ △ 4

Set 13 Exercise 5

1. Consider the practical applications of the experiments described in the passage. Why would it be important to know how quickly cars can come to a complete stop, and who would use this information?

4   **4**

Set 14 Exercise 1

Under certain conditions, hydrogen and oxygen gas can be mixed together to form H_2O. Students performed the following experiment to study the formation of H_2O.

The chemistry students fitted a gas syringe with a sparking device, then filled the syringe with different levels of H_2 and O_2 gas. The syringe plunger was then locked in place, and the gases were sparked. The resulting reaction caused water to form inside the syringe. Finally, the plunger was released, and the gas in the syringe was allowed to adjust to room temperature and pressure. The final volume of the gas was recorded and analyzed to determine its composition. Table 1 shows the results of this experiment with varying initial levels of O_2 and H_2.

The Ideal Gas Law suggests that the number of molecules of gas is proportional to the volume of that gas. The volume data in Table 1 is consistent with the following chemical equation.

$$2H_2(g) + O_2(g) \longrightarrow 2H_2O(l)$$

	Table 1			
	Volume (mL)			
Trial	H_2 (initial)	O_2 (initial)	H_2 (final)	O_2 (final)
1	20	10	0	0
2	20	30	0	20
3	20	40	0	30
4	10	30	0	25
5	50	15	20	0

Set 14 Exercise 2

1. What trial had the greatest difference between the initial H_2 volume and the final H_2 volume?
    A. Trial 2
    B. Trial 3
    C. Trial 4
    D. Trial 5

2. Which pair of trials had the same final volume of H_2?
    F. Trials 1 & 5
    G. Trials 2 & 5
    H. Trials 3 & 4
    J. Trials 4 & 5

3. According to Table 1, what was the final volume of O_2 in Trial 1?
    A.   0 mL
    B. 10 mL
    C. 20 mL
    D. 30 mL

4   **4**

Set 14 Exercise 3

1. What trial had the highest final volume of H_2?

    A. Trial 2
    B. Trial 3
    C. Trial 4
    D. Trial 5

2. What trial had the lowest volume of gases initially?

    F. Trial 1
    G. Trial 2
    H. Trial 3
    J. Trial 4

3. What was the initial O_2 volume in Trial 4?

    A.   0 mL
    B. 10 mL
    C. 25 mL
    D. 30 mL

4 △ △ △ △ △ △ △ △ △ 4

Set 14 Exercise 4

1. Based on the passage:
   - Did the H_2 and O_2 react to form H_2O when the syringe contents adjusted to room temperature, when the plunger was locked, or when the gases were ignited with the sparker?
   - Indicate how much initial H_2 was used in the first trial.

4 △ △ △ △ △ △ △ △ △ 4

Set 14 Exercise 4

2. Based on the passage, choose the statements that correctly describe the experiment. Write in the blank next to each statement to indicate whether it is supported or unsupported by the passage.

The amount of heat applied to the syringe varied for each trial.

_____

The results of the experiment contradict the Ideal Gas Law.

_____

A sparking device was used to ignite the gases.

_____

The experiment involved breaking down liquid water molecules into H_2 and O_2 gas.

_____

Water molecules were formed as a result of the chemical reaction.

_____

The initial volume of the gases varied for each trial.

_____

4 △ △ △ △ △ △ △ △ △ 4

Set 14 Exercise 5

1. Suppose the students wanted to test the reverse process, breaking down H_2O into the two gases H_2 and O_2. Write a paragraph describing how this experiment would be different from the one described in the passage and why.

4   △ △ **4**

Set 15 Exercise 1

In a science experiment, a student focused on student health at his high school. He collected urine samples from 4 student volunteers both in the morning and in the evening. The samples were then analyzed. Table 1 and Table 2 show the volume, coloration, specific gravity, and the concentration of suspended solids of the morning and evening urine samples, respectively.

The formula used for specific gravity was as follows:

$$\text{Specific gravity} = \frac{\text{density of sample}}{\text{density of water}}$$

The normal range for the specific gravity of urine is 1.0001 to 1.035.

Table 1				
	Morning urine sample			
Student	volume (mL)	color‡	specific gravity	suspended solids (g/L)
A	125	4	1.029	79.52
B	250	4	1.018	45.37
C	318	3	1.024	68.83
D	420	1	1.005	16.42

‡ Color is assigned on a scale of 0 (very pale) to 5 (very dark).

Table 2				
	Evening urine samples			
Student	volume (mL)	color‡	specific gravity	suspended solids (g/L)
A	140	4	1.025	64.88
B	275	2	1.014	41.12
C	325	2	1.021	52.19
D	450	0	1.001	2.78

‡ Color is assigned on a scale of 0 (very pale) to 5 (very dark).

4 △ △ △ △ △ △ △ △ △ 4

Set 15 Exercise 2

1. What was the volume of urine collected from Student B in the morning?

    A. 125 mL
    B. 250 mL
    C. 275 mL
    D. 420 mL

2. What was the volume of urine collected from Student C in the evening?

    F. 318 mL
    G. 325 mL
    H. 420 mL
    J. 450 mL

3. From which student was the most urine collected in the morning and evening combined?

    A. Student A
    B. Student B
    C. Student C
    D. Student D

4 △ △ △ △ △ △ △ △ △ 4

Set 15 Exercise 3

1. What was the concentration of suspended solids in the urine collected from Student C in the morning?

   A. 16.45 g/L
   B. 52.19 g/L
   C. 68.83 g/L
   D. 79.52 g/L

2. What was the specific gravity of the urine collected from Student D in the evening?

   F. 1.001
   G. 1.005
   H. 1.014
   J. 1.025

3. Which two students had approximately the same level of coloration of their urine in the morning?

   A. Students A & B
   B. Students A & C
   C. Students B & C
   D. Students C & D

4 △ △ △ △ △ △ △ △ △ 4

Set 15 Exercise 4

1. In the blank next to each statement, indicate if it is supported or unsupported by the passage.

Specific gravity is equal to the density of the
urine sample divided by the density of water.

_____

A range of 1.001 to 1.035 is a normal specific
gravity for urine.

_____

Table 2 shows the volume and coloration in
morning samples.

_____

Table 1 includes data on the specific gravity and
protein content of student urine.

_____

The color scale for the urine samples lets 0
represent very pale and 5 represent very dark.

_____

Urine samples were collected from eight students.

_____

4 △ △ △ △ △ △ △ △ △ 4

Set 15 Exercise 4

2. Based on Tables 1 and 2, give **ONE** similarity between Student B and Student C's urine samples. Be sure to compare **BOTH** students in your answer.

4 △ △ △ △ △ △ △ △ 4

Set 15 Exercise 5

1. Suppose data had been recorded about the fluid and water intake of the student volunteers. How would this affect the data gathered and the conclusions drawn from the experiment?

4 △ △ △ △ △ △ △ △ △ 4

Set 16 Exercise 1

A biology instructor is teaching a lesson on oceanic shrimp. Some oceanic shrimp are vertical migrators. Most populations of vertically migrating shrimp are found at the bottom of their depth range during the day and then move to the top of their depth range at night.

The biology teacher presented her students with a chart (Table 1) showing the depth ranges and water, protein, carbohydrate, and lipid content of three vertically migrating (vm) species of shrimp along with three non-migrating (nm) species for comparison purposes.

			Percent dry weight		
Species	Depth range (m)	Water content (% weight)	protein	lipid	carbohydrate
vm A	350–550	78.1	62.5	24.1	0.6
vm B	20–350	77.7	60.4	18.1	0.8
vm C	100–400	79.2	61.5	13.8	0.7
nm A	500–1,000	76.1	37.4	37.1	0.5
nm B	550–1,000	76.3	42.1	37.4	0.5
nm C	600–1,100	75.7	36.1	48.7	0.8

Table 1

4 △ △ △ △ △ △ △ △ △ 4

Set 16 Exercise 2

1. What is the depth range of vm A ?
   A. 20–350 m
   B. 100–400 m
   C. 350–550 m
   D. 500–1,000 m

2. What is the water content of nm C ?
   F. 75.7%
   G. 76.3%
   H. 77.7%
   J. 78.1%

3. What is the percentage of protein content of vm C ?
   A. 36.1%
   B. 61.5%
   C. 62.5%
   D. 75.7%

4   **4**

Set 16 Exercise 3

1. What is the depth range of nm A ?
    A. 20–350 m
    B. 100–400 m
    C. 350–550 m
    D. 500–1,000 m

2. Which of the following species has the least depth range?
    F. vm B
    G. vm C
    H. nm B
    J. nm C

3. Which species has the highest percentage of lipid content?
    A. vm B
    B. vm C
    C. nm B
    D. nm C

4 △ △ △ △ △ △ △ △ △ 4

Set 16 Exercise 4

1. Based on Table 1, order the four shrimp species below from the species having the lowest water content to the species having the highest water content. Write 1, 2, 3, or 4 in each blank.

nm B _____

vm C _____

nm A _____

vm A _____

4 △ △ △ △ △ △ △ △ △ **4**

Set 16 Exercise 4

2. A student claims that a shrimp species with a depth range of 175–300 m should be classified as a non-migrating shrimp. Based on the passage and Table 1, explain why the student's claim is **INCORRECT**. As part of your explanation, give the depth range of at least two species appearing in Table 1.

4 △ △ △ △ △ △ △ △ △ 4

Set 16 Exercise 5

1. Imagine you are a scientist tasked with researching the effects of diet and available food sources on vertically migrating and non-migrating shrimp. Write a paragraph explaining how you could use the data presented in the passage in your research or experiment.

4 △ △ △ △ △ △ △ △ △ 4

Set 17 Exercise 1

Students in a physics class used 2 different methods to calculate the total stopping distance of a vehicle (Z). Z is the total distance a vehicle travels from the time the driver first reacts to the emergency all the way until the car comes to a complete stop.

In Method 1, X is the distance a car travels during the driver's assumed reaction time of 0.75 seconds. Y is the average distance traveled once the brakes are applied.

Method 2 simply assumes that Z is the initial speed in feet per second times 2 seconds. (Z = speed × 2). Table 1 shows X, Y, and Z for several different initial speeds, where Z is calculated using both methods. Figure 1 is a graph of Z versus initial speed for Methods 1 and 2.

Table 1					
Initial speed (mi/hr)	Initial speed (ft/sec)	Method 1			Method 2
		X(ft)	Y(ft)	Z(ft)	Z(ft)
25	36	28	25	53	72
50	74	56	100	156	148
75	110	84	275	359	220
100	148	112	450	562	298

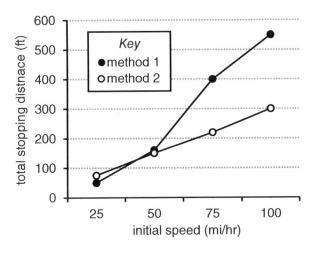

Figure 1

103

4   **4**

Set 17 Exercise 2

1. During the driver's assumed reaction time, how far does the car travel with an initial speed of 74 ft/sec ?

    A. 56 ft
    B. 84 ft
    C. 100 ft
    D. 156 ft

2. Per Method 2, what is the total stopping distance for a car with an initial speed of 100 mi/hr ?

    F. 112 ft
    G. 298 ft
    H. 450 ft
    J. 562 ft

3. What is the average distance traveled by a car while the brakes are applied if the car's initial speed is 50 mi/hr ?

    A. 100 ft
    B. 148 ft
    C. 156 ft
    D. 275 ft

4 △ △ △ △ △ △ △ △ △ 4

Set 17 Exercise 3

1. What is the average distance traveled by a car while the brakes are applied if the car's initial speed is 110 ft/sec ?

   A. 84 ft
   B. 275 ft
   C. 298 ft
   D. 359 ft

2. During the driver's assumed reaction time, how far does the car travel with an initial speed of 75 mi/hr ?

   F. 84 ft
   G. 112 ft
   H. 275 ft
   J. 359 ft

3. According to Method 2, illustrated in Figure 1, which of the following quantities is closest to the distance that a car would travel with an initial speed of 85 miles per hour?

   A. 100 ft
   B. 150 ft
   C. 250 ft
   D. 400 ft

4 △ △ △ △ △ △ △ △ △ 4

Set 17 Exercise 4

1. Based on the passage, give **ONE** difference between the description of Method 1 and the description of Method 2. Be sure to use **BOTH** methods in your answer.

4 △ △ △ △ △ △ △ △ 4

Set 17 Exercise 4

2. A student claims that a car with an initial speed of 50 ft/sec will have a higher Z value in Method 2 than a car with an initial speed of 110 ft/sec. Based on the passage, explain why the student's claim is **INCORRECT**. As part of your explanation, give the Z values according to Method 2 for cars traveling at these two initial speeds.

4 △ △ △ △ △ △ △ △ △ 4

Set 17 Exercise 5

1. The data in Figure 1 shows that the higher the initial starting speed, the more distance a car needs to come to a complete stop in an emergency. Develop a hypothesis for why that might be, and write a paragraph explaining your reasoning.

4 △ △ △ △ △ △ △ △ 4

Set 18 Exercise 1

Under certain conditions, hydrogen and oxygen gas can be mixed together to form H_2O. Students performed the following experiment to study the formation of H_2O.

The chemistry students fitted a gas syringe with a sparking device, then filled the syringe with different levels of H_2 and O_2 gas. The syringe plunger was then locked in place and the gases were sparked. The resulting reaction caused water to form inside the syringe. Finally, the plunger was released, and the gas in the syringe was allowed to adjust to room temperature and pressure. The final volume of the gas was recorded and analyzed to determine its composition. Table 1 shows the results of this experiment with varying initial levels of O_2 and H_2.

The Ideal Gas Law ($PV=n\mathrm{R}T$) suggests that the number of molecules of gas is proportional to the volume of that gas. The volume data in Table 1 is consistent with the following chemical equation.

$$2H_2(g) + O_2(g) \longrightarrow 2H_2O(l)$$

Table 1				
	Volume (mL)			
Trial	H_2 (initial)	O_2 (initial)	H_2 (final)	O_2 (final)
1	20	10	0	0
2	20	30	0	20
3	20	40	0	30
4	10	30	0	25
5	50	15	20	0

4 △ △ △ △ △ △ △ △ △ 4

Set 18 Exercise 2

1. What trial had the highest volume of gases initially?
    A. Trial 2
    B. Trial 3
    C. Trial 4
    D. Trial 5

2. According to Table 1, what was the final volume of H_2 in Trial 5 ?
    F. 0 mL
    G. 15 mL
    H. 20 mL
    J. 50 mL

3. What trial had the highest final volume of O_2 ?
    A. Trial 2
    B. Trial 3
    C. Trial 4
    D. Trial 5

4   4

Set 18 Exercise 3

1. What was the initial H_2 volume in Trial 3 ?
   A. 0 mL
   B. 20 mL
   C. 30 mL
   D. 40 mL

2. What was the initial O_2 volume in Trial 3 ?
   F. 15 mL
   G. 20 mL
   H. 30 mL
   J. 40 mL

3. Which trials had the same final volume of O_2 ?
   A. Trials 1 & 5
   B. Trials 2 & 5
   C. Trials 3 & 4
   D. Trials 4 & 5

4 △ △ △ △ △ △ △ △ △ 4

Set 18 Exercise 4

1. Based on Table 1, order the four trials below from the trial having the least final volume of O_2 to the trial having the largest final volume of O_2. Write 1, 2, 3, or 4 in the blank.

Trial 2 _____

Trial 3 _____

Trial 4 _____

Trial 5 _____

4 △ △ △ △ △ △ △ △ △ 4

Set 18 Exercise 4

2. Based on the passage:

- Does the chemical equation provided in the text represent the Ideal Gas Law, the reaction occurring in the experiment, or the reaction causing the plunger to spark and ignite?

- How many trials of the experiment were performed?

4 △ △ △ △ △ △ △ △ 4

Set 18 Exercise 5

1. Imagine you are asked to run a new and improved version of this experiment. Write a paragraph describing what changes you would make and why. How would your changes affect the results and the usefulness of the information given in Table 1?

4   **4**

Set 19 Exercise 1

In a science experiment, a student focused on student health at his high school. He collected urine samples from 4 student volunteers both in the morning and in the evening. The samples were then analyzed. Table 1 and Table 2 show the volume, coloration, specific gravity, and the concentration of suspended solids of the morning and evening urine samples, respectively.

The formula used for specific gravity was as follows:

$$\text{Specific gravity} = \frac{\text{density of sample}}{\text{density of water}}$$

The normal range for the specific gravity of urine is 1.0001 to 1.035.

Table 1				
	Morning urine samples			
Student	volume (mL)	color[‡]	specific gravity	suspended solids (g/L)
A	125	4	1.029	79.52
B	250	4	1.018	45.37
C	318	3	1.024	68.83
D	420	1	1.005	16.42

[‡] Color assigned on a scale of 0 (very pale) to 5 (very dark).

Table 2				
	Evening urine samples			
Student	volume (mL)	color[‡]	specific gravity	suspended solids (g/L)
A	140	4	1.025	64.88
B	275	2	1.014	41.12
C	325	2	1.021	52.19
D	450	0	1.001	2.78

[‡] Color assigned on a scale of 0 (very pale) to 5 (very dark).

4   **4**

Set 19 Exercise 2

1. What was the color assignment of the urine collected from Student D in the morning?

    A. 1
    B. 2
    C. 3
    D. 4

2. What was the color assignment of the urine collected from Student A in the evening?

    F. 1
    G. 2
    H. 3
    J. 4

3. Which student had the highest concentration of suspended solids in his or her urine?

    A. Student A
    B. Student B
    C. Student C
    D. Student D

4 △ △ △ △ △ △ △ △ △ 4

Set 19 Exercise 3

1. What was the concentration of suspended solids in the urine collected from Student A in the evening?
   A. 2.78 g/L
   B. 41.12 g/L
   C. 64.88 g/L
   D. 79.52 g/L

2. What was the specific gravity of the urine collected from Student B in the morning?
   F. 1.001
   G. 1.014
   H. 1.018
   J. 1.029

3. Which two students' urine had a specific gravity between 1.012 and 1.022 in the evening?
   A. Students A & C
   B. Students A & B
   C. Students C & D
   D. Students B & C

4 △ △ △ △ △ △ △ △ △ **4**

Set 19 Exercise 4

1. Based on Tables 1 and 2, give **ONE** difference between Student A's morning and evening urine samples. Be sure to compare **BOTH** samples in your answer.

_____

_____

_____

_____

_____

_____

_____

_____

_____

_____

_____

_____

_____

_____

_____

_____

_____

_____

_____

_____

_____

_____

4 △ △ △ △ △ △ △ △ △ 4

Set 19 Exercise 4

2. Based on the tables only:
   - Compared to the other student samples, did
     Student A have a morning urine sample with a specific gravity that was the highest, lowest, or neither?
   - Indicate the lowest specific gravity value for the morning samples.

4 △ △ △ △ △ △ △ △ △ 4

Set 19 Exercise 5

1. Suppose the volume of the urine samples had not been recorded in the experiment. Write a paragraph explaining how you think this would affect the data and conclusions drawn from the experiment.

4 △ △ △ △ △ △ △ △ △ 4

Set 20 Exercise 1

A biology instructor is teaching a lesson on oceanic shrimp. Some oceanic shrimp are vertical migrators. Most populations of vertically migrating shrimp are found at the bottom of their depth range during the day and then move to the top of their depth range at night.

The biology teacher presented her students with a chart (Table 1) showing the depth ranges and water, protein, carbohydrate, and lipid content of three vertically migrating (vm) species of shrimp along with three non-migrating (nm) species for comparison purposes.

			Percent dry weight		
Species	Depth range (m)	Water content (% weight)	protein	lipid	carbohydrate
vm A	350–550	78.1	62.5	24.1	0.6
vm B	20–350	77.7	60.4	18.1	0.8
vm C	100–400	79.2	61.5	13.8	0.7
nm A	500–1,000	76.1	37.4	37.1	0.5
nm B	550–1,000	76.3	42.1	37.4	0.5
nm C	600–1,100	75.7	36.1	48.7	0.8

Table 1

4   **4**

Set 20 Exercise 2

1. What is the depth range of nm B ?
    A. 100–400 m
    B. 500–1,000 m
    C. 550–1,000 m
    D. 600–1,100 m

2. What is the water content of nm A ?
    F. 75.7%
    G. 76.1%
    H. 76.3%
    J. 79.2%

3. What is the percentage of lipid content of vm B ?
    A. 13.8%
    B. 18.1%
    C. 24.1%
    D. 37.1%

4   **4**

Set 20 Exercise 3

1. Which of the following species has the greatest depth range?

   A. vm B
   B. vm C
   C. nm B
   D. nm C

2. Which species has the lowest percentage of protein content?

   F. vm B
   G. vm C
   H. nm B
   J. nm C

3. Which two species have the highest percentage of carbohydrate content?

   A. vm B & nm B
   B. nm B & nm C
   C. vm A & nm B
   D. vm B & nm C

4 △ △ △ △ △ △ △ △ △ 4

Set 20 Exercise 4

1. A different shrimp species, vm D, is found at a depth of 450 m at night. Use the information in the text and Table 1 to predict an approximate depth range for vm D. Explain how you used the passage to make your prediction.

4 △ △ △ △ △ △ △ △ 4

Set 20 Exercise 4

2. Based on the table, give **ONE** difference between vertically migrating and non-migrating shrimp. Do **NOT** use the difference of vertical and non-migration or the difference in depth range in your answer.

4 △ △ △ △ △ △ △ △ 4

Set 20 Exercise 5

1. Imagine that a column of data has been accidentally left off of Table 1. What added information would be useful for further understanding the oceanic shrimp? Write a paragraph describing what possible type of measurements could make the data more complete and useful.

4 △ △ △ △ △ △ △ △ △ 4

Set 21 Exercise 1

A group of researchers attempted to develop a new technique for vertical farming by constructing three artificially heated and humidified chambers. The researchers found the weekly average air temperature in Celsius (°C) and the weekly average humidity in percent water vapor in each of the three chambers. The results for the first six weeks of their measurements are given in Table 1 and Table 2.

Table 1			
	Weekly average air temperature (°C)		
Week	Chamber 1	Chamber 2	Chamber 3
1	20.01	19.12	18.87
2	20.13	19.13	18.85
3	20.36	19.13	18.88
4	20.68	19.15	18.92
5	20.95	19.22	18.98
6	21.02	19.20	19.03

Table 2			
	Weekly average humidity (%)		
Week	Chamber 1	Chamber 2	Chamber 3
1	84%	83%	78%
2	84%	82%	77%
3	85%	81%	76%
4	86%	82%	76%
5	88%	80%	78%
6	87%	79%	79%

4 △ △ △ △ △ △ △ △ **4**

Set 21 Exercise 2

1. The highest weekly average humidity recorded during the first six weeks of the study was:

   A. 86%
   B. 87%
   C. 88%
   D. 89%

2. What was the average air temperature in the three chambers in Week 4 ?

   F. 18.15°C
   G. 18.59°C
   H. 19.58°C
   J. 20.69°C

3. Which of the following statements best describes the relative conditions of the three chambers in the first six weeks of the study?

   A. Chamber 1 had high average air temperature and high average humidity; Chamber 2 had low average air temperature and low average humidity; and Chamber 3 had medium average air temperature and medium average humidity.
   B. Chamber 1 had low average air temperature and medium average humidity; Chamber 2 had medium average air temperature and low average humidity; and Chamber 3 had high average air temperature and high average humidity.
   C. Chamber 1 had high average air temperature and low average humidity; Chamber 2 had medium average air temperature and high average humidity; and Chamber 3 had low average air temperature and medium average humidity.
   D. Chamber 1 had high average air temperature and high average humidity; Chamber 2 had medium average air temperature and medium average humidity; and Chamber 3 had low average air temperature and low average humidity.

4 △ △ △ △ △ △ △ △ △ 4

Set 21 Exercise 3

1. Which of the following statements best describes the change in weekly average air temperature in Chamber 2 ?

   A. The weekly average air temperature increased or stayed the same consistently from Week 1 to Week 6.

   B. The weekly average air temperature decreased from Week 1 to Week 3 and increased or stayed the same from Week 3 to Week 6.

   C. The weekly average air temperature increased or stayed the same from Week 1 to Week 5 and decreased from Week 5 to Week 6.

   D. The weekly average air temperature decreased or stayed the same from Week 1 to Week 4 and increased from Week 4 to Week 6.

2. Suppose the rate of growth of crops in each of the vertical farming chambers is determined by either weekly average air temperature, weekly average humidity, or both. If the growth rate in Chamber 2 greatly exceeds the growth rate of Chambers 1 and 3, which of the following statements would one be justified in concluding?

   F. High weekly average air temperature and high weekly average humidity are ideal for plant life growth rate.

   G. Medium weekly average air temperature and medium weekly average humidity are ideal for plant life growth rate.

   H. Low weekly average air temperature and low weekly average humidity are ideal for plant life growth rate.

   J. All of the above conclusions can be justified.

3. Based on Table 2, as the number of weeks increased, the weekly average humidity in Chamber 3:

   A. increased only.

   B. decreased only.

   C. first decreased, then increased.

   D. varied with no general trend.

4 △ △ △ △ △ △ △ △ △ 4

Set 21 Exercise 4

1. Based on the passage, choose the statements that correctly describe the experiment. In the blank next to each statement, indicate if it is supported or unsupported by the passage.

Measurements were recorded for six different chambers.

_____

Tables 1 and 2 show measurements for weekly average air temperature and precipitation.

_____

Measurements were taken for six consecutive weeks.

_____

Each week, Chamber 1 had consistently higher average air temperature than Chamber 3.

_____

The average humidity in Chamber 2 decreased each week.

_____

Vertical farming is an agricultural method involving three artificially heated and humidified chambers.

_____

4 △ △ △ △ △ △ △ △ 4

Set 21 Exercise 4

2. Based on the data for Chamber 3 in Table 1:

• Did Week 6 have the highest, lowest, or the same average air temperature of all the weeks measured for that chamber?

• Indicate the lowest average air temperature for Chamber 3.

4 △ △ △ △ △ △ △ △ △ 4

Set 21 Exercise 5

1. If the researchers had kept a particular plant in each chamber and kept a record of its growth as well as the temperature and humidity in each chamber, do you think this would enhance or detract from the usefulness of the data? Write a paragraph defending your stance.

4 △ △ △ △ △ △ △ △ △ 4

Set 22 Exercise 1

Solar panels are assemblies of connected photovoltaic cells that harness solar energy to produce electricity. Photovoltaic cells can produce electricity from a range of light frequencies at varying efficiencies; however, current solar panel technology is incapable of capturing the entire solar range. Scientists have determined that illuminating photovoltaic cells with monochromatic light enables higher efficiency, but they have yet to develop the technology necessary to split light into its various wavelength ranges to make use of this higher efficiency.

Study 1

Photovoltaic cells show a decrease in efficiency at increased temperatures. A group of scientists wanted to determine which frequency of light might produce the best efficiency in photovoltaic cells and how temperature might affect this efficiency. The results of their study are given in Table 1.

Study 2

With mathematical models, the same group of scientists attempted to project the efficiencies of photovoltaic cells coupled with techniques that allowed for the splitting of wavelength ranges. They projected uniform increases in efficiencies for all frequencies, but they noted the continued decrease in efficiency at increased temperatures. The theoretical results of their models are given in Table 2.

Table 1			
Temp. (°C)	Photovoltaic cell efficiency (%)		
	Frequency 1	Frequency 2	Frequency 3
25	20.2%	20.0%	20.4%
26	19.7%	19.7%	19.7%
27	19.2%	19.4%	19.0%
28	18.7%	19.1%	18.3%
29	18.2%	18.8%	17.6%

Table 2			
Temp. (°C)	Theoretical photovoltaic cell efficiency with wavelength splitting (%)		
	Frequency 1	Frequency 2	Frequency 3
25	47.2%	45.0%	50.4%
26	46.1%	44.3%	48.6%
27	45.0%	43.6%	46.8%
28	43.9%	42.9%	45.0%
29	42.8%	42.2%	43.2%

Set 22 Exercise 2

1. Do the results from Study 1 support the claim that photovoltaic cells capturing different frequencies function at varying efficiencies with changes in temperature?

   A. Yes, because as temperature increases, so does efficiency.
   B. Yes, because as temperature increases, efficiency decreases.
   C. No, because there is no uniform change in efficiency as related to temperature.
   D. No, because all photovoltaic cells function at the same efficiency regardless of frequency.

2. Based on the results from Study 1, photovoltaic cells capturing which frequency of light would function best in environments that keep the cell temperatures at roughly 29 degrees Celsius?

   F. Frequency 1
   G. Frequency 2
   H. Frequency 3
   J. No frequency will function better in these environments.

3. Based on the results from Study 1, photovoltaic cells capturing which frequency of light would function best in environments that keep the cell temperatures at roughly 26 degrees Celsius?

   A. Frequency 1
   B. Frequency 2
   C. Frequency 3
   D. No frequency will function better in these environments.

4 △ △ △ △ △ △ △ △ 4

Set 22 Exercise 3

1. One of the scientists suggests that he can build a cooling system for the theoretical photovoltaic cells in Study 2, which will keep the cells 1 degree Celsius cooler than normal but decrease their efficiency by 1%. The theoretical photovoltaic cells capturing which frequencies, if any, would benefit from this cooling system?

   A. Frequencies 1 & 2
   B. Frequencies 2 & 3
   C. Frequencies 1 & 3
   D. None of the theoretical photovoltaic cells would benefit.

2. In Study 1, which of the following variables is held constant?

   F. The temperature of the environment.
   G. The photovoltaic cells used.
   H. The frequency of light captured by the photovoltaic cells.
   J. No variables were held constant.

3. Suppose the scientists note the temperature sensitivity of the photovoltaic cells in both experiments, defining sensitivity as the amount of change in efficiency as temperature increases. Which of the following best describes the changes in efficiency and temperature sensitivity of the photovoltaic cells from Study 1 to the theoretical photovoltaic cells with wavelength splitting in Study 2 ?

   A. Efficiency increases from Study 1 to Study 2, and sensitivity to temperature increases from Study 1 to Study 2.
   B. Efficiency increases from Study 1 to Study 2, but sensitivity to temperature decreases from Study 1 to Study 2.
   C. Efficiency decreases from Study 1 to Study 2, and sensitivity to temperature decreases from Study 1 to Study 2.
   D. Efficiency decreases from Study 1 to Study 2, but sensitivity to temperature increases from Study 1 to Study 2.

4 △ △ △ △ △ △ △ △ 4

Set 22 Exercise 4

1. Based on Study 2 and Table 2:

    • Do the results shown in Table 2 represent percent of photovoltaic cells, percent of wavelength splitting, or theoretical percent efficiency?

    • What is the highest percent value shown in Table 2?

4 △ △ △ △ △ △ △ △ △ 4

Set 22 Exercise 4

2. Based on Table 1, order the four temperatures below from the temperature corresponding to the lowest efficiency for Frequency 1 to the temperature corresponding to the highest efficiency for Frequency 1. Write 1, 2, 3, or 4 in the blank.

28°C _____

25°C _____

29°C _____

27°C _____

4 △ △ △ △ △ △ △ △ △ **4**

Set 22 Exercise 5

1. Examine the passage and consider which parts were difficult for you to understand and which parts were easier. Create a list of at least five things and explain why each item on your list was difficult or easy for you. Then, write 2–3 sentences brainstorming some actions you can take to improve your understanding and fluency on science passages.

4 ▲ ▲ ▲ ▲ ▲ ▲ ▲ ▲ 4

Set 23 Exercise 1

The *doubling time* of a bacterium is the amount of time it takes for a given sample to double in quantity of organisms. A biology student performed three activities involving four bacteria: *E. coli, Salmonella, Streptococcus, and Shigella.*

Activity 1

The student prepared 4 nutrient broths (A, B, C, D), which he then poured into petri dishes. He allowed cultures of the bacteria to grow independently in each petri dish and measured the doubling time (in minutes) of each bacterium in each nutrient broth. The results appear in Table 1.

Table 1				
	Doubling time (min)			
Broth	*E. coli*	*Salmonella*	*Streptococcus*	*Shigella*
A	17	18	26	40
B	19	21	29	43
C	20	22	33	46
D	16	17	24	36

Activity 2

The student then prepares 3 lightboxes where he places samples of each bacterium held in Broth D. He allows the bacteria to grow under yellow, blue, and red light and measures each sample's doubling time under each light. The results appear in Table 2.

Table 2				
	Doubling time (min)			
Light	*E. coli*	*Salmonella*	*Streptococcus*	*Shigella*
Yellow	16	17	24	36
Blue	15	16	23	35
Red	17	18	25	37

Activity 3

The student finds the equation $A = Pe^{kt}$ describes the growth of these populations accurately. The equation states that population is determined by initial population multiplied by the natural number (e) taken to an exponent of time, in hours, by the growth constant of the bacteria. The student finds the growth constant of each bacteria in blue light by setting $k = \dfrac{\ln(2)}{t}$. The results appear in Table 3.

Table 3	
E. coli	k = 2.773
Salmonella	k = 2.594
Streptococcus	k = 1.808
Shigella	k = 1.188

4 △ △ △ △ △ △ △ △ △ 4

Set 23 Exercise 2

1. Based on Activity 1, which of the nutrient broths appears to produce the slowest doubling time for the bacteria populations?

   A. Broth A
   B. Broth B
   C. Broth C
   D. Broth D

2. If the student needed to produce a very large sample of a bacteria population as quickly as possible, which bacteria species should he grow under which light?

   F. *E. coli* under blue light
   G. *Salmonella* under blue light
   H. *Streptococcus* under red light
   J. *Shigella* under yellow light

3. According to Activity 2, if the student began growing a population of 1,000 *Salmonella* bacteria under red light, he should expect to have 4,000 in how many minutes?

   A. 30
   B. 32
   C. 34
   D. 36

4 △ △ △ △ △ △ △ △ **4**

Set 23 Exercise 3

1. In working with the bacterial growth equation in Activity 3, the student notices a correlation between the growth constant k and the doubling time of the bacterial populations. Which of the following correlations is most likely true?

   A. As k increases, doubling time increases.
   B. As k increases, doubling time decreases.
   C. As k increases, doubling time is unaffected.
   D. There is no correlation between k and doubling time.

2. If the student were to introduce a fifth bacterium into Activity 2 with a doubling time of 28 minutes in Broth D under yellow light, which of the following doubling times (in minutes) might he most likely expect the fifth bacterium to have under blue light?

   F. 27
   G. 28
   H. 29
   J. 30

3. Given the fifth bacterium's doubling time of 28 minutes under yellow light, it likely has a growth constant k between which two bacteria?

   A. *E. coli* and *Salmonella*
   B. *Salmonella* and *Streptococcus*
   C. *Streptococcus* and *Shigella*
   D. This cannot be determined.

4 △ △ △ △ △ △ △ △ △ 4

Set 23 Exercise 4

1. In an activity similar to Activity 2, a different light color is tested with the same bacteria. The doubling time for *E. coli* is found to be 14 minutes. Use the results in Table 2 to predict an approximate doubling time for *Salmonella* under this new light color. Explain how you used the information provided to make your prediction. Then, indicate if *Streptococcus* would have a shorter or longer doubling time than *Salmonella* under this light.

4 △ △ △ △ △ △ △ △ △ 4

Set 23 Exercise 4

2. Based on the passage, give **ONE** similarity between the description of Activity 1 and the description of Activity 2. Be sure to include **BOTH** activities in your answer.

4 △ △ △ △ △ △ △ △ △ 4

Set 23 Exercise 5

1. Suppose a student prepared a petri dish for each bacterium in Activity 1 that contained no broth and recorded the doubling time for each bacterium. Would this be an improvement or an unnecessary addition to the experiment? Write a paragraph explaining your answer.

4 △ △ △ △ △ △ △ △ △ **4**

Set 24 Exercise 1

Stars begin their lives composed of roughly 70% hydrogen. Nuclear fusion of hydrogen atoms in a star's core drives the majority of energy and luminosity. After the majority of hydrogen has been exhausted from the star's core, the star enters into the red giant branch and begins the fusion of hydrogen in the surrounding shell, as well as the fusion of helium in its core. The hydrogen in the surrounding shell is quickly exhausted, as is the helium in the core, and near the end of the star's life, it begins to fuse hydrogen and then helium in its outermost shell until all of it is exhausted. The figure below shows the percentage of hydrogen present in a star over the course of its life cycle.

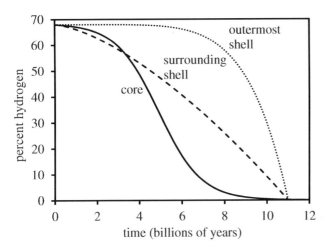

Figure 1

4 △ △ △ △ △ △ △ △ △ 4

Set 24 Exercise 2

1. Based on the figure, the percent hydrogen in the surrounding shell after 8 billion years will be closest to which of the following:

   A. 30%
   B. 35%
   C. 40%
   D. 45%

2. Based on the figure, at how many billions of years will there be roughly 0% hydrogen remaining in the core?

   F. Between 6 and 7
   G. Between 7 and 8
   H. Between 8 and 9
   J. Between 9 and 10

3. After the fusion of hydrogen is exhausted in the core and fusion of hydrogen begins in the surrounding shell, the fusion of helium begins in the core. Which of the following is most likely true about the percent helium in the core as time increases?

   A. The percent helium decreases over time.
   B. The percent helium increases over time.
   C. The percent helium does not change over time.
   D. The percent helium over time cannot be determined.

4 △ △ △ △ △ △ △ △ **4**

Set 24 Exercise 3

1. Around 28% helium is present in a star's core at the beginning of its lifetime. A scientist hypothesizes that the amount of helium present begins to drop only after the percent hydrogen present in the core drops below 20%. According to this hypothesis, which of the following is the best graphical representation of the percent helium over time?

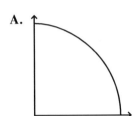
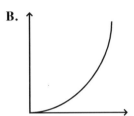
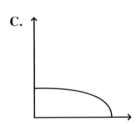
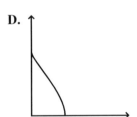

2. After 11 billion years, if the star has spent the majority of its life in the main sequence and the most recent 1 billion years in the red giant branch, the star will shed nearly all of its mass and become a white dwarf, surviving for billions of years before fading out. Which of the following most likely catalyzes this event?

   F. The exhaustion of hydrogen in the core.
   G. The exhaustion of hydrogen and helium in the core.
   H. The exhaustion of hydrogen in the core, and the exhaustion of helium in the shells.
   J. The exhaustion of hydrogen in the shells and the exhaustion of helium in the shells and core.

3. In Figure 1, as the number of years increases, the percent hydrogen in the surrounding shell:

   A. increased only.
   B. decreased only.
   C. remained the same.
   D. varied, but with no general trend.

4 △ △ △ △ △ △ △ △ 4

Set 24 Exercise 4

1. Based on the passage, choose the statements that correctly describe nuclear fusion during a star's life cycle. In the blank next to each statement, indicate if it is supported or unsupported by the passage.

Stars are composed of about 70% helium at the start of their life cycle.

_____

Nuclear fusion begins in the star's core.

_____

Helium atoms provide most of the star's energy and luminosity.

_____

Nuclear fusion of hydrogen atoms in the star's core is followed by the fusion of helium atoms.

_____

Fusion of hydrogen and helium occurs in the outermost shell at the beginning of a star's life.

_____

At the end of its life, a star will fuse hydrogen and helium atoms in the outermost shell until both are exhausted.

_____

4 △ △ △ △ △ △ △ △ △ 4

Set 24 Exercise 4

2. Based on the passage, give **ONE** difference between the nuclear fusion of hydrogen atoms in a star and nuclear fusion of helium atoms in a star. Be sure to compare **BOTH** types of atoms in your answer.

4 △ △ △ △ △ △ △ △ △ 4

Set 24 Exercise 5

1. Imagine that hydrogen is not available in the star for nuclear fusion. How would this affect the star's life cycle? Write a paragraph explaining what you think would happen.

Contributors

Content Director
Oliver Pope

Lead Content Editor
Lisa Redmond

Question Editors
Michael Laird, Irit Maor, Eric Manuel

Question Writers
Alex Levy, April Chow, Chad Sziszak, Chris Husson, Colin Takita, Dan Marchese, Eric Manuel, Tyler Munson, Wendy Seidl, Sam Knight, Sean Neuerburg, Lisa Redmond, Langley Pierre

Layout
Jeff Garrett, Elaine Broussard, Eliza Todorova, Eric Manuel

Proofreaders
Eric Manuel, Allison Eskind, Stephanie Bucklin, Michael Laird

Interns
Kaitlyn Mattox, Rashaud Red, Jamaica Rhoden, Chelsey Smith

MasteryPrep is created by Craig Gehring

Made in the USA
Lexington, KY
27 November 2019